CINDERELLA

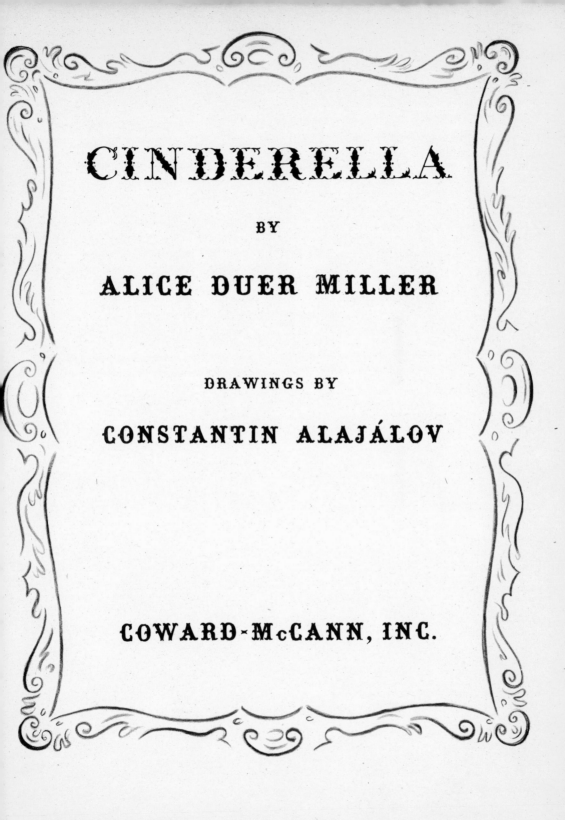

CINDERELLA

BY

ALICE DUER MILLER

DRAWINGS BY

CONSTANTIN ALAJÁLOV

COWARD-McCANN, INC.

Poor Cinderella
   Lost her pretty mother
When she was a baby,
   Only four or five.
She and her father,
   Clinging to each other,
Lived in the memory,
   Keeping it alive.

But when a heart
   Is really truly broken
No little daughter
   Can take away the pain;
Nothing can be done,
   Nothing can be spoken
That will make him happy
   Or a playfellow again.

So this sad man thought:
   "This must have an ending;
She must not be shadowed
   By the sorrow of my life.
Poor Cinderella,
   She needs a woman's tending.
I must do my duty,
   I must take a wife."

II

There was a lady in the neighborhood,
A widow, badly off, accounted sage,
With two young daughters, who, he understood,
Were just about his Cinderella's age—
Well-mannered little girls, who blew their nose
And said their prayers exactly as they ought
And bobbed their curtsies and turned out their toes—
One played the harp, one the piano-forte,
And both spoke French and German, knew a bit
Of Greek and Latin; both could dance with grace
Quadrilles and minuets, and both could knit,
Crochet, do cross work, petit-point and lace.
They seemed ideal friends for Cinderella—
Gismonda one, the other Isabella.

He told this lady that his heart was dead
And buried; but he passionately desired
A mother for his child, and she, he said,
Seemed just the woman that the part required.
As he was handsome, rich and much esteemed,
He did not plead in vain—or very long;
The lady snapped him up—she, too, it seemed,
Was sad and lonely and could use a strong
Man's hand to guide her and her little brood.
Ah, what a tender mother she would make!
Poor man, almost at once he understood
That he had made a terrible mistake
In marrying coldly from a sense of duty,
For loveless marriage lacks all truth and beauty.

The lady was not really good and kind,
Her heart was bitter, though her words were honey;

She had a narrow, angry, stubborn mind,
And an insane, unmastered love of money.
He saw it all too late—the girls were proud
And scorned his daughter's innocence and youth;
They whispered giggling, or they laughed out loud,
Making her feel unmannered and uncouth.
His mind was slowly turning to divorce,
Or separation from his unloved bride;
Alas, one morning in the Park, his horse
Stumbled and fell on him, and thus he died.

Poor Cinderella, now being deserted
Was to a kitchen drudge at once converted.

III

Cinderella was awfully pretty; her eyes
Were that wonderful color you see when the skies
Are clouded in Autumn, except shining through
Is a patch—only one—of a bright vivid blue.
Her hair was a shade between golden and brown,
And she braided it all round her head in a crown.
She was slender and graceful and not very tall;
Her hands and her feet were delightfully small.
Yet nobody noticed her beauty at all!

The reason for this was no further to seek
Than the fact that she worked every day in the week.
She rose before sunrise and lit a small taper
And put out the kitten and took in the paper
And made up the fire and put on the kettle
To be sure there'd be time for the coffee to settle.
Then she turned out the parlor and swept down the
 stairs
And mopped up the hall, which was black and white
 squares
And gave Cinderella a great deal of trouble;
Then, hearing the coffee beginning to bubble,
She ran to the kitchen as fast as her legs
Could take her and—timing them—put on the eggs.
She got out the butter and toasted the bread.
(She had set the three trays before going to bed,
For nothing, you know, will get done of itself.)
Now she lifted them carefully down from the shelf
And, laying the food on the plates in a trice,
She ran up three flights, and she ran up them thrice,
So fast that the toast had no time to get cold;
Then she pulled back the curtains and, straightening
 each fold,
She said in a gentle affectionate way:
"It's time to wake up, and a very fine day."

She never stopped working the way she began,
She did the full job of five maids and a man.
Yet her sisters contrived when the long day was
 ended
To leave her some stockings and gloves to be
 mended—
Nice work, they explained, they would do it with
 pleasure
Themselves, but she saw that they hadn't the leisure;
And at last as she stole to her attic to bed,
She passed those proud girls on the stairway, who
 said,
As they went to a party in new satin sashes,
"My dear, I believe she was born in the ashes!"

IV

Rat-a-tat! Rat-a-tat!
Who in the world can be knocking like that?
Rat-a-tat! It's wakened the cat.
Quick, Cinderella, what is that girl at?
Answer the door, can't you? Rat-a-tat!

She opened the door at the last rat-a-tat,
And there was a soldier, erect on the mat;
He was certainly six foot eleven in height,
He'd a helmet and plume, and his breeches were
    white,
He wore black shiny boots that came up to his hip,
He had spurs on his heels, a mustache on his lip,
He had gold epaulets on his bright scarlet coat,
And, saluting, he gave Cinderella a note.
It was large, pink and square, quite a beautiful
    thing,
And she saw in the corner, the arms of the King!

V

The monarch of this country had a son
And heir, who would of course be king some day.
He as a child was loved by everyone,
But now he had been many years away,
Studying with tutors, traveling to and fro,
Learning the things that princes have to know.

Not only spelling and arithmetic
And all those things *you* learnt when you were
    young,
But abstruse subjects—conics, Arabic—
And fluency in every modern tongue,
And how to be the darling of his nation
And keep the army up without taxation,

And how to be polite and good at games,
Patient and always punctual at meals,
How to remember everybody's names,
To stop and wonder how your neighbor feels.
He also learned to be remote and haughty,
If anyone were pushing, pert or naughty.

Now he was coming home to take up life
Beside his father with its many duties,
And his first duty was to find a wife
Among his country's galaxy of beauties.
So to save time, the old King asked them all
To a great brilliant, dazzling palace ball.

VI

"Mother," said dark-browed Gismonda,
  "What shall I wear to the ball?"
Shall I wear corn-colored satin,
  With my cob-web Valenciennes shawl?
Or mauve tulle with scarlet geraniums—
  That would look well at the ball."

"Mother," said cold Isabella,
  "What do you think I should wear?
Silver brocade or pink velvet,
  With a chaplet of pearls in my hair?
Apple green silk and the emeralds—
  You'd lend me your emeralds to wear."

"I shall wear black," said their mother,
  "Black lace and diamonds, I think.
You, my adorable Bella,
  Will be lovely in rose-colored pink.
Gismonda's complexion looks better
  In yellow than lilac, I think."

Though trembling, up spoke Cinderella:
"Mightn't I go to the ball?"
The three women stared at her blankly,
And then gave a laugh, one and all—
"Are you out of your mind, Cinderella?
Our kitchen maid go to the ball!"

VII

The great night has arrived, and you haven't a notion
Of the general excitement and fuss and commotion.
The coiffeur is there
To do everyone's hair,
And he says with an air
Of conviction: "O, Ciel,
Ma chère Mademoiselle,
With your hair done by me you are perfectly belle!"
Now I'm sorry to say while he's doing the curls
Of these very unkind and unamiable girls
They are quarreling over their emeralds and pearls:
"My dear Isabella, you must be aware
That emeralds and pink with your carroty hair . . ."
"Oh, how do you dare,
To say that my hair . . ."
"But it is." "No, it's not, but I'll answer you back,
If it were, it is better than dank greasy black."

And every few minutes, a shout and a scream:
"Cinderella,
I can't find my lotion and cream."
"Cinderella,
Fetch a stick or a club
Fetch a cane or umbrella,
At once, for my lipstick rolled under the tub."

Cinderella ran upstairs to help them, and tore
Downstairs the next minute to answer the door.
Their dresses came home in the prettiest boxes,
And their cloaks, made of sable and ermine and
        foxes.
Oh, such a rustling

Of paper, and bustling
Unpacking them, praising them, looking and fussing
And getting them over their heads without mussing
Their finished coiffures . . . "Cinderella, take care,
Stand up on a chair,
Or you'll ruin my hair."

At last they were ready, with fan and bouquet
And handkerchief scented with eau de Cologne;
They got into their coach and were driven away,
And poor Cinderella was left all alone.
She went down to the kitchen, and there, it appears,
She sat down by the ashes and burst into tears.

VIII

Now let us pause a moment to reflect
　　How you and I in crises can behave
Nobly—more nobly than you would expect—
　　And prove ourselves resourceful, cool and brave,
But when the crisis passes, very often
Our nerves collapse, our courage seems to soften.

So now with Cinderella. At her best
　　She had been patient, kind, and stout of heart
Getting her step-mother and sisters dressed,
　　Until at last she heard their coach depart;
Then as there seemed no point in being brave
Alone, self-pity drowned her like a wave.

"Poor Cinderella, poor dear girl," she thought.
　　"Nobody loves or cares for her at all.
Why should she not be going as she ought
　　Like other ladies to the Prince's ball?
They will be sorry when they find her dying..."
And suddenly a voice said: "Stop that crying."

A strange old lady stood within the door,
　　Her pale hands folded on her ebon stick,
Upon her head a cone-shaped cap she wore,
　　A long cape wrapped her, and her eyes were quick
And darted from one corner to the other.
"I am," she said, "your fairy god-mother."

Our heroine remembered having heard
That the most powerful fairy on this earth
Had been her father's friend, and had conferred
Honor by standing sponsor at her birth;

But as she never saw the Fairy, grew
To think the story probably untrue.

"Why," asked the Fairy, "do you weep alone?"
   "Because I wanted, oh, so much to go
And see the Prince, the ball, the King, the
         throne . . .
   Like other girls."
                  "And so you shall."
                              "Oh, no,
Impossible.

            There's nothing I could wear."
"Nonsense, my dear. You're just as good as there."

IX

The Fairy's black stick
Was uncommonly quick
When called on to do any magical trick.
Now it hopped and it jumped,
And it banged and it thumped,
And the Fairy, remaining quite still on the mat,
Said: "Abracadabra," or something like that.

X

You would have been completely
   Astonished at the change
That came about so neatly,
   For it was very strange—
The watcher by the fire,
   The drudge, the kitchen maid,
In glorious attire
   Was instantly arrayed.

Her hair was curled and braided
   And shone like burnished gold;
Her skirt so old and faded,
   Her blouse so torn and old,
Were gone and in their places
   A dress as white as snow,
All net and frothy laces,
   And flounce and furbelow.

Her fan was ostrich feather,
   Her gloves were long and white,
Her bodice held together
   By diamond buttons bright;
They did not know of zippers,
   In those old days, alas;
Yet, strange to say, her slippers
   Were made of plastic glass.

XI

Now the stick with a sort
Of a grunt and a snort,
Gallumphed, thumped and humped itself out to the
    court,
Where a pumpkin of very unusual size
Was ripening before being made into pies.
You will easily surmise
Cinderella's surprise,
When the stick seemed to rise
And point at the pumpkin,

                which at its approach
Became of a sudden a gilt and glass coach!

Is the fear in your mind
That the stick couldn't find
Any steeds for that gold coach to travel behind?
No, nothing like that!
With a dab and a pat
At a shadow that once was a large Chinese rat,
And then at another, and then at two more,

The stick with no trouble at all changed the four
Gray rats into cream-colored horses, so round
And dappled, with manes that were braided and
    bound
With red ribbon, and tails that flowed to the ground.

All people who heeded
The fashions conceded
That for coaches in those days, two footmen were
    needed,
To sit at the back, looking proud and superior,
And make all who walked feel intensely inferior.
And a coachman of course was a *sine qua non*.
(That means something without which you cannot
    get on.)
Now the Fairy had noticed three nice little mice

In a trap, and she pointed her stick at them thrice,
And said Abracadabra or something like that,
And—Presto—a coachman in lace and cocked hat,
And two footmen appeared, very stately and tall;

So now Cinderella was ready with all
The fixings required to go to the ball.
She ran to her coach and was going to hop in it,
When her god-mother said, rather sternly: "One
    minute!
One minute, my dear! And I beg of you pay
The strictest attention to what I now say:
Be off to your ball which you so much desired
To see—flirt and dance, be observed, be admired
By all—break a couple of hearts if you like,
But I warn you, be sure that before the clocks strike
The hour of midnight, you're back in this house.
For at twelve every footman will change to a mouse,
Your coach to a pumpkin, your dress and your cloak
Will be ragged and torn once again on the stroke
Of the hour of midnight. Each cream-colored horse
Will become . . ."
                "But dear god-mother, listen, of
        course,
I'll do just as you say. I'll be here on the dot
Of the hour. What a wretch I should be were I not,
Considering your wonderful kindness to me!
How could I forget what you told me?"
                                "Well, see
That you don't. Now get into your coach—drive
        away
To the ball, and enjoy it. Be good and be gay."

XII

The entrance to the palace,
  A stairway high and wide,
Was banked with palms and roses
  And lilies on each side;
And scores and scores of candles
  In crystals overhead,
And on the stair a carpet
  Of glorious cherry red.

As Cinderella mounted,
  So slim and young and straight,
And just a little breathless,
  For she was rather late,
As she ran up the stairway
  In diamonds and lace,
The Prince himself descended,
  And met her face to face.

She glanced at him with pleasure,
  For he was such a man
As young girls dream of meeting,
  But very seldom can;
And then remembering manners,
  She turned her gaze aside,
But he stood still and blocked her way,
And stared with eyes that seemed to say,
"By all the saints to whom I pray,
I never thought to see this day;
Stay lovely vision, angel, stay,
  For I have found my bride!"

They stood like this a moment,
  As if alone, and then
The Prince, with better breeding
  Than ordinary men,
Recovered his composure,
  And said with royal charm:
"Princess, unknown but welcome,
  Accept, I beg, my arm."

You can perhaps imagine
  The wonder and the stir,
When through the ballroom doorway
  The Prince came in with her,
So radiant and lovely,
  And not one noble dame
Could tell her rank or country
  Or even knew her name.

Her step-mother and sisters,
  They even did not guess
That this admired stranger,
  This beautiful princess,
So splendidly attired,
  So graceful and polite,
Was that unhappy maiden,
  They worked from dawn to night.

And everywhere were whispers:
  "The Duchess Geraldine,

From green Pamphylia's mountains?"
    "Oh, no, the youthful queen
Of distant Hyperborea,
    Where unicorns run wild."
"As usual you've got the thing
All wrong—she's child to Atheling
That wicked rich old pirate-king—
    His one beloved child."

Of all the wild excitement,
   The Prince seemed unaware;
His face was calm and joyous,
   He seemed to tread on air,
He had the look and manner,
   Of one bewitched, entranced,
While he and Cinderella
   Just danced

and danced

and danced.

XIII

People wiser than you—or even than I—
Assure us that Time passes steadily by,
Doesn't linger or lag, doesn't stand still or fly.
But it's hard not to feel that it hastens its pace
When we play with some friends in a wide grassy
    place,
At I-Spy, Hide-and-Seek, Tag, or Prisoners' Base.
It's hard not to think it stands perfectly still
When we sit in a chair with a molar to fill
And the dentist gets out that detestable drill.

So now Cinderella glanced up now and then
At the clock in the tower—the palace Big Ben—
And saw it was ten—it was half after ten—
And then she forgot, till she saw with a shock
That made her heart beat and her head reel and
    rock—
It was midnight—one minute before by the clock!

XIV

Almost midnight! She gave a gasp
And wrenched her hand from the Prince's clasp.
How wrong she had been, how very wrong
To forget the time, and stay so long!
Almost midnight—the hour of doom!
Away she ran through the crowded room,
And reached the stair, as the clock in the tower
Donged the first stroke of the fatal hour.

In the lower hall, the palace cat,
Asleep on her paws and old and fat,
Blinked her eyes at three little mice,
Scuttling away as the clock struck twice.
Out in the court-yard, the palace hound,
Nosing about where bones were found
Sometimes, saw with acute surprise
Four gray rats of gigantic size.
And a kitchen-boy going home to bed
Noticed a pumpkin as big as his head,
Down on the ground where the coaches stood.
It looked so yellow and large and good
That he picked it up in his arms and took it
Back to the house for his mother to cook it.

But nobody—boy or hound or tabby
Noticed a figure slim and shabby
That darted running with all her might
Across the court-yard into the night.

XV

The Prince could hardly understand—
Gone? Without a word of parting.
Wrenching away her hand,
Dodging and darting
Away through the crowd on the dancing-floor,
Slipping out of the ball-room door,
So that now he saw her no more—no more.

He tried to follow, but found his way
Blocked by courtiers who wanted to say:
"Sir, if I may
Express myself, what a charming ball!"
"Your Highness, who is the unknown beauty?
Who is the lady all
Admire? Who is that fair princess?"

The Prince had been taught that a prince's duty
Is courtesy—*toujours la politesse*.
He couldn't insult and cut them short
And hurt the feelings of half his Court;
He couldn't elbow and push and shove
Out of the room to follow his love.

And so by the time he reached the stair
No one was there.
He asked the grooms in the hall below:
"Did anyone see a lady go
Away in her coach?"
                              "Your Highness, no,
Not a lady has left; not a coach has stirred."
Nobody thought to say a word
Of the only guest who had departed,

A kitchen wench, who had fled like a bird.
So the poor Prince turned and, heavy-hearted,
Went slowly back to rejoin the merry
Throng, and as he mounted the cherry
Carpet, he came to the very place
Where first he had seen her lovely face;
As he paused to consider how shy and sweet
She had seemed to him then, it came to pass
That he dropped his eyes, and at his feet
Was a tiny slipper—a slipper of glass.

XVI

Some people, you know, the day after a party
    Feel flat, uninspired, depressed, at loose ends,
And not in a mood to be chatty and hearty
    And tell all the news to their stay-home friends.
But others enjoy with a zest partly spiteful
    Explaining to those who were not on the list
That the ball was entrancing, exciting, delightful,
    Select—Oh, my dear, you don't know what you
        missed!

Cinderella's proud sisters were eager to tell her
  The fun they had had while she slumbered in bed,
The flowers, the palace from attic to cellar,
  What the ladies had on, what the gentlemen said.
They dwelt at some length on their personal glory,
  How they danced every dance—never sat down
    at all,
And of course they went into the wonderful story
  Of the Vanishing Stranger—the belle of the ball.

Her hair and her eyes—they described every
    feature—
  Every gesture, they said, was a model of grace.
At this Cinderella, the innocent creature,
  Ran out of the room with a very red face.
But she thought to herself as she sat by the embers:
  "I wish I had asked if he minded my flight—
Though of course, I imagine, he hardly remembers
  A girl who ran off without saying good night."

XVII

In this town, all the ladies who thought themselves
    chic
Had a custom of staying at home once a week
And expecting their friends to drop in and partake
Of tea or hot chocolate, and crumpets and cake.

On this day Cinderella was never required
To answer the bell, for a footman was hired
From the caterer's shop, a tall, insolent fella,
But much more impressive than poor Cinderella.
It was also made clear, that she must not appear
Downstairs while a single guest lingered, for fear
She should put them to shame by her manners un-
    couth;
But I don't need, I'm sure, to explain that the truth
Was they feared that her glorious beauty and youth
Would throw them decisively into the shade,
And of course they had reason for being afraid.

XVIII

The guests had gone,
   The hour was late,
When a coach and four
   Drove up to the gate,
And out of it stepped a splendid peer—
   The Prince's Aide,
   The Duke of Belgrade!
Now what in the world was he doing here?

Cringing and civil,
   The caterer's groom
Showed him up
   To the drawing-room
Where the two proud sisters and their mother
   Were sitting alone,
   Their guests all gone,
Unctuously praising one another.

The Duke in the doorway,
   Rather stern,
Quietly bowed
   To each in turn.
"Ladies," he said, "my pleasant duty
   Is to come at the King's command—
   You see this slipper in my hand?
I seek its owner—the vanished beauty.

"Did any of you
   At the palace ball
Drop this shoe
   In the palace hall?
"If so I beg of you not to hide
   The truth, for my master swore
   That only she, the lady who wore
This slipper, shall be his bride."

XIX

Gismonda's feet were square and huge,
   Gismonda's feet were tender,
And yet she wildly tried to scrooge
   Into that slipper slender.
She stamped and pulled, and pulled again,
She shoved with all her might and main,
But it was utterly in vain:
   She could not get it on.

Pale Bella's feet were long and flat
    And rather given to blisters,
But they were narrower at that
    A little than her sister's.
This gave her hope and was the source
Of stronger efforts, greater force.
She screamed with pain, and yet of course
    She could not get it on.

The Duke looked down with scorn on all
    These struggles wild and frantic.
The slipper looked so very small,
    Those four feet so gigantic.
At last he stooped and took it back;
He was afraid that it might crack
Under the sisters' mad attack,
    Trying to get it on.

XX

The Duke, who had still many visits ahead,
Was eager to go, so he bowed and he said:
"I am right, am I not? You three ladies are all
The ladies who went from this house to the ball?"
"That's right," said the ladies, "just us—just us three."
But a voice from the doorway said softly: "There's
    me."

The Duke saw beside him what really did seem
Like a child in an apron, but fair as a dream.
(In telling the story, which year after year
He told very often, he always made clear
To his listeners, he did not immediately guess
That this beautiful child was the vanished princess;
But he said that he felt it his obvious duty
To give one fair chance to so perfect a beauty.)
"She's mad," cried Gismonda, with scorn. "She's in-
        sane,"
Cried Bella. Their mother said: "Let me explain."
And stretching her mouth till she thought that she
        smiled,
She added: "My step-daughter's only a child.
I naturally could not permit her to go
To a ball—at her age—and she didn't, I know.
In the first place she'd nothing whatever to wear."
"And yet," said the Duke, "I believe she was there."

Cinderella meantime had sat down in a chair
With her gentle demure and yet competent air,
And the Duke, who had seemed so indifferent and
        grand,
Now knelt at her feet with the shoe in his hand
And fitted it on without struggle or bother.
And then she produced from her pocket the other—
Its mate—and looked up with a twinkle of fun
At the Duke, who said: "Perfect! My mission is
        done."

"No, no," cried Gismonda. "That slavey—that
    chit . . ."
And so angry was she, she fell down in a fit.

"No, no," said her mother. "You're hardly acquainted
With her pitiful past . . ." and so saying she fainted.

Isabella, however, contrived to keep cool.
"My dear Duke!" she exclaimed. "Don't behave like
    a fool.

Consider, I beg, that it wouldn't be wise
To take back our maid to your prince as a prize.
Poor half-witted creature—poor ignorant drudge . . ."
But the Duke answered coldly: "The Prince must be
    judge."

XXI

Gallop, gallop through the street—
Fire struck from the horses' feet—
Gallop, gallop, the great coach swings
From side to side on its leather springs.
And Cinderella inside of it sits
Silent, but frightened out of her wits,
Her clasped hands tense with her wild distress
For fear that the Prince will like her less
In her faded apron and shabby dress,
Will say: "This isn't my lost princess;
This isn't the belle of the palace ball.
No, no, it isn't the girl at all."

XXII

The coach—it was one of the King's golden coaches
    With his arms on the door and a crown on the top,
To which every groom runs when he sees it ap-
        proaches—
    Raced up to the palace and came to a stop.
The Duke with an air at once humble and splendid
    Stepped out and then offered an elegant hand
To assist Cinderella, who also descended,
    So weak in the knees that she hardly could stand.

For the stairway that seemed to stretch far up to
        heaven
    Was solid with footmen in powder and lace,
And a huge Major-Domo, who must have been seven
    Feet tall, with a look of contempt on his face—
A look guaranteed to inspire cold terror
    In all who beheld it, and now seemed to say:
"This shabby young woman? A palpable error.
    One moment, I beg, while I send her away."

XXIII

And now within the palace
  A cry of joy was heard,
And down the Prince came skimming
  As lightly as a bird.
And timid Cinderella
  Abandoned her alarms;
The Prince was wholly unaware
  Of all the footmen standing there,
And for the Major-Domo's stare
  He really did not seem to care,
But with a high, triumphant air,
  He clasped her in his arms.

"My beautiful, my darling,"
  He said, "the cruel pain
Of losing you was almost worth
  The finding you again."
And Cinderella answered:
  "Oh, dear, it cannot be
Two people ever were in love
  As much as you and me!"

He led her up the stairway,
  He led her through the hall,
Past many golden drawing-rooms
  With mirrors on the wall,
He led her to his father
  The old King, stern and wise,
And Cinderella thought: "Alas,
  What am I in his eyes?

"A shabby little maiden,
  But late a kitchen wench.

Suppose he says, my son must wed
  A peeress, Slavic, French,
From distant Hyperborea,
  From green Pamphylia far ...”
But what the old King said was: “Child,
  How beautiful you are!”
He made her sit beside him,
  He held her tiny hand,
He told her of the noble gems,
  Awaiting her command.
She tried to say that love alone
  Mattered a jot or tittle,
But yet her smile betrayed the fact
  Gems mattered just a little.

XXIV

What did Gismonda—what did Isabella
Do, when they found their slavey, Cinderella,
Had won the Prince? Did they upon the spot
Become the palace darlings? They did not.
The King, like many kings, was spoilt, and more
Than armed enemies, he feared a bore.
Those ladies bored him. "No, my dear," he said,
"If they should dine here, I should go to bed."
The Prince took higher ground, but he poured fuel
Upon his father's hatred—they'd been cruel
To Cinderella. He could not forgive
The wretchedness in which they made her live.
So she, who would not hurt a cat or dog,
Would slip away and visit them incog
And smile, remembering all her griefs and labors,
And bring them gifts that they could show their
        neighbors,
And boast—and say—"You see this lovely dress?
A present from her Highness the Princess..."
"Just think our little sister—near the throne—"
"My step-daughter, but dearer than my own..."
And then they'd hint, for they were really hateful,
That Cinderella showed herself ungrateful—
Her head was turned, she did not seem aware
How much she owed their early love and care.
All this repeated with a tang of malice
Made the Prince vow that never in his palace
Should they set foot—the palace doors were barred:
But Cinderella, anything but hard,
Managed to smuggle them an invitation
Just to the church, but not to the collation.

XXV

The wedding was something that cannot be told,
　Such flowers and jewels as never were seen;
Cinderella's long train, made of ermine and gold,
　Was held up by three beauties, and each one a
　　queen.
The Prince in white satin, with touches of red
　In his plume, set all feminine hearts in a flame.
"She'd be lucky to get him," the peeresses said,
　"If he hadn't a crown, or a cent to his name."

The Fairy, a very old friend of the King's,
  Though rather a haughty and critical one,
Rode in on her stick—so much faster than wings—
  To bless the young couple and join in the fun.
And if anyone dared in her presence to say
  Cinderella was lucky to make such a catch,
She said: "Not at all—it's the opposite way—
  Your Prince is the one who has made a good
    match."

And everyone danced in the city for days
    And nights, for the city was lit for a week,
And everyone shouted such hip-hip-hurrays
    That no loyal subject was able to speak.
There were feasting and fireworks, music and laugh-
      ter;
    The national happiness couldn't be hid.
And the Prince and the Princess lived happy there-
      after,
    The storybook says, and I think that they did.

40